Race into the SATs at full stretch with CGP!

This brilliant CGP Stretch book is full of extra-challenging fiction texts and questions — perfect for confident pupils who have already mastered our Fiction SAT Buster! All eight reading elements are fully covered:

- **2a** Word Meanings
- **2b** Fact Retrieval
- **2c** Summarising
- **2d** Inferences
- **2e** Predictions
- **2f** Structure
- **2g** Language
- **2h** Comparisons

There are separate question pages for each element, so it's simple for pupils to spot what they're being asked to do.

What's more, the fun Tellastaurius tick boxes ask pupils to assess how they're doing, so you'll have an easy way to keep track of their progress.

Published by CGP

Editors: Izzy Bowen, Emma Crighton, Catherine Heygate, Holly Robinson
Reviewer: Samantha Bensted

With thanks to Alison Griffin and Sean Walsh for the proofreading.
With thanks to Jan Greenway for the copyright research.

ISBN: 978 1 78294 834 6

Clipart from Corel®
Printed by Elanders Ltd, Newcastle upon Tyne.

Based on the classic CGP style created by Richard Parsons.

Text, design, layout and original illustrations
© Coordination Group Publications Ltd. (CGP) 2017
All rights reserved.

Playground Problem

Louise Young and her friends love going to the playground in their local park. But when a terrible storm puts the playground out of action, Louise must find a way to solve her town's playground problem...

What to do —

1) Open out the folding pages, and read the story *Playground Problem*.

2) Then read it one more time to make sure that you've really understood it.

3) Take a couple of minutes to see if you can pat your head and rub your tummy at the same time. Now you're fully prepared to tackle the questions.

Turn the page.

| 2b | *Fact Retrieval Questions* |

6. How did Louise find out that the local council was responsible for the playground?

....

1 mark

7. How did Alfonso Brighthorn help Louise's school?

....

1 mark

8. How long after the storm did Louise's party take place?

Tick **one** box.

one day ☐

one week ☐

one month ☐

one year ☐

1 mark

9. Why did Louise invite Suman Patel to the party?

Explain your answer fully.

....

....

....

....

....

3 marks

Tellastauriuses have special powers for answering fact retrieval questions. How did you find them?

Inference Questions

INFERENCE questions ask you to think a bit more deeply about what's going on in the text. Have another read of 'Playground Problem' and then see if you can answer these questions.

1. **'Louise bit the crust with a grin.'**

   a) How do you think Louise felt here?

   ....

   1 mark

   b) Why did she feel like this?

   ....

   1 mark

2. Read the paragraph that starts **'She sat by the window...'**

   What evidence is there that the storm was very powerful? Give **two** examples.

   ....

   ....

   2 marks

3. After the storm, why were there buckets in the school corridors?

   ....

   1 mark

4. Look at page 4. Find and copy a phrase which suggests that the children were upset when they saw how the storm had affected the playground.

   ....

   1 mark

5. How do you think Louise felt when she read the council's response to her first letter? Support your answer with evidence from the text.

   ....

   ....

   2 marks

2d	# *Inference Questions*

6. Read the paragraph beginning **'At school, the fair had gone well...'**

Find and copy a phrase which suggests that Alfonso Brighthorn's actions were very important for the school.

....

1 mark

7. **'It took days of nervous planning to organise the party...'**

Why do you think Louise felt nervous while she was organising the party?

....

....

....

2 marks

8. How can you tell that lots of people turned up to the party? Give **one** way.

....

1 mark

9. Why did Louise read the headline **'gleefully'**?

....

....

2 marks

10. How does the text make Louise seem determined? Give **one** way.

....

....

1 mark

Tellastauriuses can make inferences faster than you can say "reading is great". How did these pages go?

2a Word Meaning Questions

WORD MEANING questions pick out some of the trickier words from the text and ask you to explain what they mean. Take a deep breath and then have a go at this batch of questions.

1. '"A colossal storm will be making its way in..."'

   What does the word **'colossal'** tell you about the storm?

   ....

   | 1 mark |

2. 'The damage caused by the storm was catastrophic.'

   Which of the words below is closest in meaning to **'catastrophic'**?

   | terrible | obvious | small | angry |

   | 1 mark |

   Circle your answer.

3. Read the paragraph beginning **'At school, the fair had gone well...'**

   Find and copy a word from this paragraph that means 'luckily'.

   ....

   | 1 mark |

4. 'They resolved to hold a party at the playground...'

   What is the meaning of the word **'resolved'** in this sentence?

   | refused | decided | expected | demanded |

   | 1 mark |

   Circle your answer.

Tellastauriuses eat word meaning questions for breakfast. Sometimes for lunch too. How about you?

Section 1 — Playground Problem

2c   *Summary Questions*

SUMMARY questions can be pretty tricky — they ask you to bring together information from more than one paragraph in the text. Test your summarising skills with these questions.

1. Read page 3. This part of the text is about

the school's response to the storm	Louise's feelings about school	the storm and its impact	the damage to the playground

1 mark

Circle your answer.

2. Read from '**This gave Louise her second brainwave...**' to '**...made Louise's stomach churn.**'

Which sentence best summarises these two paragraphs?

The council changes its mind.	Louise organises a party.	Suman Patel writes an article.	Louise contacts a reporter.

1 mark

Circle your answer.

2e   *Prediction Question*

To answer PREDICTION questions, you need to think about what might happen next in the story. Remember to use details from the text to support your answer. Try this question.

1. Do you think the council will repair the playground? Explain your answer.

....

....

....

2 marks

Really good Tellastauriuses can rip these questions to pieces. Tick to show how you got on with them.

Holiday on Hill Farm

This story is about a boy called Tobi who goes to stay on a farm for a holiday. That might sound like fun to some people, but Tobi thinks it sounds terrible. Then the farmer, Joe, has the idea to introduce him to someone who might make him feel quite differently...

What to do —

1) Open out the folding pages, and read the story *Holiday on Hill Farm*.

2) When you've done that, practise your special party trick — maybe you can roll your tongue, or play some great air guitar.

3) Then read the text again before moving on to try the questions.

Turn the page. ➡

Holiday on Hill Farm

A powerful smell of manure flooded the car as Tobi and his family bumped along the rough track towards Hill Farm. Tobi pinched his nose tight, hoping to block out the stench that was rapidly filling his lungs. He had spent the whole trip from Birmingham refusing to look out of the window, determinedly ignoring the sights of buildings and streets giving way to picturesque fields and streams. He wanted to spend his time playing video games with his friends or going to the park, not hanging around on an old farm with nothing to do. Between the mud, flies and lack of mobile phone signal, it was the worst possible location for a holiday.

For the full length of the journey, Tobi had carried out his own small rebellion by defiantly tuning out his mum's remarks about the animals in the fields, or his dad's suggestion that they sing a cheery song to get themselves into the holiday spirit. Instead, he had stared silently at the back of his dad's headrest for the entire journey.

As the car stopped at the farm, Tobi caught a glimpse of the farm's owner, Joe, who his parents had been friends with for the last fifteen years. Tobi reluctantly slid out of the car, flinching as he almost stepped in a cowpat that had flies hovering greedily above it. He lingered behind the adults as they chatted, glancing at the mud and hay strewn around the farmyard with dismay. Even though he'd been to the farm before, he'd only been a toddler at the time — the only thing he could remember about the experience was having to be scrubbed from head to toe every evening to get rid of all the dirt he'd accumulated over the course of the day.

"Come on, Tobi," his mum called. Frowning irritably, he followed her through a wooden door into their cottage, which was directly opposite the farmhouse. He gazed around glumly until he spotted a shiny television in the corner, which made him feel a small glimmer of hope.

The story continues over the page. ➡

The next morning, Tobi was woken early by the screeching crow of a cockerel, and try as he might he couldn't get back to sleep. Unwilling to lie awake in bed, he decided to get dressed and go downstairs. Peering out of the kitchen window into the farmyard, he spotted Joe already up and about, decked out in long boots and a muddy jacket. Joe saw Tobi and waved him over.

"Good morning, Tobi! How are you finding your Hill Farm holiday so far?"

Tobi flushed and focused his gaze down at the ground.

"Not your kind of thing, eh? That's a shame — you used to love it here when you were little," said Joe. He ran a hand through his hair and sighed. "Well, I'm afraid I've got to be getting on. I've barely got time to catch my breath today — I hope you don't mind if I leave you to it?"

Tobi shook his head. Joe began to walk away, then hesitated, a small smile on his lips.

"Actually, I know someone who might lift your spirits — maybe you'd like to meet her?"

"Meet who?" Tobi enquired curiously.

"Our newest addition," replied Joe. "She's a sweet little lamb, but she was rejected at birth — her mother wouldn't let her feed. We've tried everything, but it's just one of those things that happens in nature sometimes. So we're hand-feeding her. Come on."

Intrigued, Tobi followed Joe into the barn. In the dim light he could make out several wooden pens filled with straw. He heard a high-pitched, mournful bleating from the furthest stall. As he leaned over the gate, he saw a tiny lamb with a fluffy coat and spindly legs looking up at him hopefully.

"It's feeding time," Joe said, digging around in a box on the floor. He pulled out a bottle, similar to the ones that Tobi had seen human babies being fed with, which was filled with a milk-like substance. Then he let himself into the pen and held the bottle out to the lamb.

The baby soon began guzzling down the liquid, her tail wagging ecstatically. After a few moments, Joe turned to Tobi.

"Want to try?"

Tobi nodded eagerly. Joe moved over and showed Tobi how to hold the bottle correctly. Tobi laughed when he felt a sharp tug on the bottle and the lamb started to drink again.

Soon the bottle was empty. Joe looked at Tobi anxiously. "What did you think?"

"It was great!" Tobi answered, grinning. "Can I feed her again sometime?"

The concern evaporated from Joe's face. "Yes — that would certainly help me out. You can be her personal carer, if you like."

Tobi punched the air and sprinted back to the cottage, bursting to share the news. On his way in, he almost collided with his mum and dad coming down the stairs in their pyjamas, bleary-eyed and with tousled hair. Tobi's words fell out like an avalanche as he explained all about encountering Joe, and the tiny lamb, and how he had fed her himself. Tobi's mum and dad glanced at each other, their mouths hanging open, before breaking into warm smiles.

Not a single complaint came from Tobi's lips over the days that followed. He was too busy with the important responsibility of making sure Sasha — as he had decided to name the lamb — was fed, clean and had enough love and attention, all under Joe's watchful eye. Sasha became quite attached to Tobi; every morning she would bleat with delight when he appeared in the doorway, and she often shadowed him around the barn like a devoted puppy.

By the end of the week's holiday, Tobi admitted that he had thought too rashly about the farm. It was always fun to play games or go to the park, but those things were nothing compared to the satisfaction of helping to raise a new-born animal — that was an experience he would never forget.

Fact Retrieval Questions

FACT RETRIEVAL questions — they're about finding key pieces of information from the text. Read the story again, then see if you can track down the answers to these questions.

1. Look at the first paragraph.

   Give **one** thing Tobi would rather do than go to the farm.

   ....

   1 mark

2. Read the paragraph beginning **'For the full length of the journey...'**

   a) What did Tobi's dad suggest doing on the journey?

   ....

   1 mark

   b) What did Tobi do instead?

   | He stared at his dad's headrest. | He went to sleep. | He played on his phone. | He read a book. |

   1 mark

   Circle your answer.

3. How long have Tobi's parents known Joe for?

   ....

   1 mark

4. What did Tobi almost do when he got out of the car?

   ....

   1 mark

5. Look at page 13.

   Write down **two** things you are told about the cottage Tobi's family stayed in.

   ....

   ....

   2 marks

2b

Fact Retrieval Questions

6. Read the paragraph beginning '**The next morning...**'

Why did Tobi go downstairs?

He wanted to watch television.	**He couldn't get back to sleep.**	**He was feeling hungry.**	**He heard Joe calling him.**

1 mark

Circle your answer.

7. Why did the lamb have to be hand-fed?

....

1 mark

8. How did Joe help Tobi feed the lamb?

....

1 mark

9. Give **two** things Tobi did as the lamb's **'personal carer'**.

....

....

2 marks

10. Put a tick in the correct box to show whether each statement is true or false.

	True	**False**
Tobi had travelled from Birmingham.		
Tobi had never been to the farm before.		
The lamb was in the nearest stall to Tobi.		
Tobi's family stayed on the farm for one week.		

1 mark

Tricky facts stick to a Tellastaurius like the world's stickiest glue. How did you find these questions?

Section 2 — Holiday on Hill Farm

18

Inference Questions

INFERENCE questions can seem tricky, but if you've read through the text and thought about it carefully you should be able to work out the answers. Have a go at these questions.

1. Look at the first paragraph. How can you tell that Tobi didn't like the smell of the farm?

    ....

    `1 mark`

2. **'...it was the worst possible location for a holiday.'**

    Is this a fact or an opinion?

    ....

    `1 mark`

3. Why do you think Tobi felt **'a small glimmer of hope'** when he saw the television?

    ....

    ....

    `1 mark`

4. How can you tell that Tobi felt embarrassed when Joe asked him how he was finding the farm? Give **one** way.

    ....

    `1 mark`

5. **'I've barely got time to catch my breath today...'**

    What does this phrase suggest about Joe?

He's not feeling well.	He woke up early.	He's not very busy.	He has a lot to do.

    `1 mark`

    Circle your answer.

Section 2 — Holiday on Hill Farm   *© CGP — not to be photocopied*

Inference Questions

2d

6. Read the paragraph beginning **'Intrigued, Tobi followed Joe into the barn...'**

    How does this paragraph make the reader feel about the lamb?

scared of it	sorry for it	confused about it	angry with it

    1 mark

    Circle your answer.

7. **'Joe looked at Tobi anxiously.'**

    Why was Joe anxious?

    Tick **one** box.

    Tobi had spilt some of the food. ☐

    He was afraid Tobi had fed the lamb incorrectly. ☐

    He wanted Tobi to like feeding the lamb. ☐

    His farm was doing badly. ☐

    1 mark

8. How can you tell that Tobi was happy when Joe asked him to be the lamb's **'personal carer'**? Give **one** way.

    ....

    1 mark

9. When Tobi's mum and dad heard about how he fed the lamb, they were both surprised and pleased.

    Explain how this is shown in the text.

    ....

    ....

    ....

    2 marks

Tellastauriuses can answer inference questions while walking backwards. How about you?

2a Word Meaning Questions

WORD MEANING questions check your vocabulary is up to scratch and that you know what words from the text mean. Read over 'Holiday on Hill Farm' again, then try these questions.

1. '...buildings and streets giving way to **picturesque** fields and streams.'

    What does the word **'picturesque'** mean in this sentence?

    | beautiful | muddy | large | ugly | **1 mark** |

    Circle your answer.

2. '...Tobi was woken early by the **screeching** crow of a cockerel...'

    Give **two** things the word **'screeching'** suggests about the cockerel's crow.

    ....

    ....

    2 marks

3. 'Actually, I know someone who might **lift your spirits**...'

    What does the phrase **'lift your spirits'** mean in this sentence?

    Tick **one** box.

    help you out ☐

    make you taller ☐

    teach you a lesson ☐

    cheer you up ☐

    1 mark

4. '...her tail wagging **ecstatically**.'

    What does the word **'ecstatically'** mean in this sentence?

    ....

    1 mark

Tellastauriuses can do word meaning questions in the twinkling of an eye. How was this page for you?

The last few questions on Holiday on Hill Farm are under here. ►

Summary Questions

SUMMARY questions ask you to think about the overall ideas in the text. They can be about the whole text or just a chunk of it. Read the story again and have a try at these questions.

1. Put these summaries of paragraphs in the order they appear in the story.

    The first one has been done for you.

    Tobi feeds a lamb for the first time. ☐

    Tobi arrives at the farm and remembers the past. ☐

    Tobi enters the barn and meets the lamb. ☐

    How Tobi and his parents spent the journey to Hill Farm. 1

    Tobi's reaction to being given an important responsibility. ☐

    Tobi's first impressions of the cottage. ☐

    1 mark

2. The main message of the story is that

lambs don't need much looking after	you shouldn't live in a city	being a farmer is the best job	things can be better than you expect

    1 mark

    Circle your answer.

Comparison Question

COMPARISON questions are like a game of spot the difference — you have to work out what's different or similar about two or more parts of the text. Have a go at this question.

1. How do Tobi's feelings about the farm change during the story?

    ....

    ....

    1 mark

Tellastauriuses can summarise and compare like no other dinosaur. How about you? Tick a box.

Theseus and the Minotaur

'Theseus and the Minotaur' is a famous myth from Ancient Greece.
It's an exciting story about a brave prince who goes to fight a
dangerous creature. The story has been told for thousands of years.

What to do —

1) Read the story *Theseus and the Minotaur*
— you'll need to turn over for some of it.

2) Do a handstand to shake all that new
information down into your head. Then,
just in case the handstand didn't work,
read the text again.

3) When that's all done, you're ready to
cartwheel through to the questions...

Theseus and the Minotaur

In a time long before any living person can remember, a hideous creature lived on the island of Crete. This violent beast, half~man, half~bull, was known to all as the Minotaur.

The Minotaur had been imprisoned for years within a winding labyrinth. Every nine years, fourteen young men and women — known as tributes — were sent to Crete from the city of Athens, at the demand of Crete's cruel king, Minos. When the tributes arrived, they were taken to the labyrinth and sacrificed to the monster within.

The people of Athens lived in terror that a son or daughter of theirs would be chosen for the next sacrifice. So, on the third selection of tributes, Theseus, the prince of Athens, volunteered to enter the labyrinth. He hoped to slay the grotesque creature and prevent it from ever harming his people again.

Along with the other tributes, Theseus set sail from Athens towards Crete and the terrible fate that awaited them. After travelling over a bright and brilliant sea, they reached their destination. The island's sandy beaches and distant mountains greeted them as they docked, but even those beautiful sights could do little to still their trembling hands or settle their fluttering stomachs.

Once on land, Theseus was led through a bustling town to King Minos's grand palace, which had hundreds of rooms and tall, blood~red columns holding up the ceilings. There, Minos himself waited, a cruel smile forming on his face as he viewed the tributes before him. His smirk deepened as he caught sight of Theseus standing tall and proud amongst the ragtag group.

That evening, Theseus was invited to attend a great feast. He tried to enjoy the taste of what might be his final meal, but he found himself distracted by the sight of the king's daughter, Ariadne, whose gaze never left him over the course of the feast.

The story continues over the page.

Later that evening, as he was settling down for the night, Theseus heard soft footsteps approaching his room. He sat up, startled, when the figure of Ariadne came out from the shadows. Ariadne silenced his lips with her finger and told him she had spoken with a man named Daedalus, who had designed the labyrinth. Daedalus knew the maze inside out, and was sure that there was no way to navigate its complex pathways. Instead, he had given her a simple ball of thread. Ariadne told Theseus that this thread would be his only hope of escaping the labyrinth's twisting tunnels. She placed the ball in his hand and closed it tight.

Theseus knew that Ariadne's father would punish her for such a betrayal. In gratitude for her aid, he promised her that she could return to Athens with him and become his wife once he had slain the beast.

The next morning, the tributes walked nervously from the palace up to the labyrinth. They were stripped of any weapons with which to fight and, once in the maze, were plunged into darkness as the entrance was sealed shut behind them. Theseus immediately sprang into action. He drew out a blade that he had hidden under his tunic, then told the other tributes to wait by the entrance. He handed one end of Ariadne's gift to the nearest of the tributes, then began to walk through the labyrinth in search of the beast, making sure to unravel the ball of thread as he went.

Moving cautiously through the tunnels, he became aware of the low, quaking rumble of the creature snoring somewhere in the maze. As he went deeper into the labyrinth, the sound of the monster grew louder. Theseus's heart began to race as he realised that it must be nearby. Suddenly, there was a rustling from within the darkness, and Theseus saw the yellow eyes of the Minotaur blink open. The beast slowly uncurled itself, revealing its formidable size as it stood to its full height. It was an unnatural creature: a hulking combination of bull and man, with sharp, pointed horns. Its eyes glared at Theseus, enraged, and it huffed heavily, flaring its nostrils.

Man and Minotaur circled each other, both poised to attack. Theseus clutched his sword tightly as he tried to work out where to strike first. Then, in one fluid movement, he raised his weapon and swung at the beast. The Minotaur roared and charged towards him. Theseus dived sideways, and the Minotaur's horns missed him by a hair's breadth. Then, as he regained his balance and turned to land another blow, the Minotaur drove towards him with its horns yet again. Theseus was forced to throw himself out of the way, swinging his sword wildly at the same time in a desperate attempt to strike the beast.

Sword and horn clashed over and over, both Theseus and the Minotaur fighting with equal ferocity. However, time was taking its toll — as each new blow struck, Theseus felt his exhaustion grow. Little by little, the Minotaur was gaining the upper hand.

Finally, inspiration struck Theseus: using the last of his strength, he threw himself forward and slid directly between the Minotaur's legs. While the monster was still bewildered, Theseus jumped up behind it and, with one powerful plunge of his sword, the battle was won. The once-mighty Minotaur lay dead and defeated on the cold labyrinth floor.

Triumphant, Theseus took the thread and followed it as fast as he could through the darkness, until it led him back to the other tributes. Together, the group used their combined might to prise open the maze's door. Outside, Ariadne jumped up, delighted to see Theseus emerge safely.

Theseus embraced her, then called for the other tributes to follow him. They ran hurriedly towards the sea, skirting around the edge of the town, until the reassuring sight of the Athenian ship came into view.

Moments later, the ship was sailing swiftly out to sea. Many of the tributes cast worried looks back towards the island, fearing the sight of sails. Theseus, however, stood confidently at the front of the boat, his eyes fixed on the horizon with a smile. Against all the odds, he had slain the Minotaur and escaped from the treacherous labyrinth. The people of Athens would sleep soundly once more, safe in the knowledge that they were finally free from the fearsome Minotaur.

 Open the flap for the start of the story.

2b

Fact Retrieval Questions

*The information for FACT RETRIEVAL questions is always somewhere in
the text — if you look carefully enough, you'll be able to find it. Try these.*

1. How often were tributes sent to the Minotaur?

    ....

    1 mark

2. How many tributes were sent to the Minotaur each time?

    ....

    1 mark

3. How many selections of tributes had there been before Theseus volunteered?

one	two	three	four

    1 mark

    Circle your answer.

4. The tributes saw **two 'beautiful sights'** when they got to Crete.

    What were they?

    ....

    ....

    2 marks

5. What was Theseus invited to do on the evening he arrived at the palace?

    ....

    1 mark

6. Who was the maze's designer?

Minos	Ariadne	Daedalus	Theseus

    1 mark

    Circle your answer.

2b

Fact Retrieval Questions

7. What did Theseus promise Ariadne? Give **two** things.

....

....

| 2 marks |

8. Read the paragraph beginning '**Moving cautiously through the tunnels...**'

a) Theseus first heard the Minotaur's

| roars | snores | steps | snarls |

| 1 mark |

Circle your answer.

b) Theseus first saw the Minotaur's

| feet | nostrils | horns | eyes |

| 1 mark |

Circle your answer.

9. '**Finally, inspiration struck Theseus...**'

What was Theseus inspired to do? Explain your answer fully.

....

....

....

| 3 marks |

10. How did Theseus use Ariadne's gift to find his way out of the maze?

Explain your answer fully.

....

....

| 2 marks |

Tellastauriuses can do fact retrieval questions whilst hopping on one leg. How did you do?

Section 3 — Theseus and the Minotaur

Inference Questions

INFERENCE questions are about what's happening beneath the surface of the story, so take a deep breath and read it again, looking for what's really going on. Then answer these questions.

1. Find and copy a phrase from the first paragraph that tells you the story took place a long time ago.

   ....

   ....

   | 1 mark |

2. '...still their trembling hands or settle their fluttering stomachs.'

   What does this phrase tell you about how the tributes were feeling?

   Tick **one** box.

   It tells you they were feeling lonely. ☐

   It tells you they were feeling nervous. ☐

   It tells you they were feeling confident. ☐

   It tells you they were feeling tired. ☐

   | 1 mark |

3. Read the paragraph beginning **'The next morning...'**

   How does the writer make it seem hard for the tributes to escape the maze?

   Give **one** way.

   ....

   | 1 mark |

4. Give **one** way Theseus was prepared for his challenge.

   ....

   | 1 mark |

2d | *Inference Questions*

5. Read the paragraph beginning **'Moving cautiously through the tunnels...'**

    How does this paragraph make the Minotaur seem frightening?

    ....

    ....

    ....

    2 marks

6. **'...the group used their combined might to prise open the maze's door.'**

    This makes the maze's door seem

    | light | short | heavy | old |

    1 mark

    Circle your answer.

7. **'They ran hurriedly towards the sea, skirting around the edge of the town...'**

    Why did the group go around the edge of the town?

    ....

    ....

    1 mark

8. How does the text make Theseus seem caring?

    Explain your answer as fully as you can.

    ....

    ....

    ....

    3 marks

Tellastauriuses can do inference questions blindfolded.
How did you get on with these? Tick a box.

Section 3 — Theseus and the Minotaur

2a

Word Meaning Questions

You don't need to know every word in the dictionary to be able to answer WORD MEANING questions, but you do need to know what the words in the text mean. Try these questions.

1. **'The people of Athens lived in terror...'**

    What does the word **'terror'** mean in this sentence?

    ....

    1 mark

2. **'In gratitude for her aid, he promised her...'**

    The word **'gratitude'** tells you that Theseus was

    | sorry | hopeful | surprised | thankful |

    1 mark

    Circle your answer.

3. Find and copy **one** word from page 24 that shows Theseus moved through the maze slowly.

    ....

    1 mark

4. **'While the monster was still bewildered...'**

    Circle the word that means the same as **'bewildered'** in this sentence.

    | angry | scared | confused | injured |

    1 mark

5. Read the paragraph beginning **'Theseus embraced her...'**

    Find and copy **one** word from this paragraph that means 'comforting'.

    ....

    1 mark

Tellastauriuses have special powers for answering word meaning questions. How did you find them?

The last few questions on <u>Theseus and the Minotaur</u> are under here. ➡

2c # *Summary Question*

Read the whole text again before trying this SUMMARY question, asking yourself how you'd describe different bits as you go. Then pick up your pen and have a go at the question.

1. Put these summaries of paragraphs in the order they appear in the story.

   The first one has been done for you.

   Why Theseus volunteered to enter the maze. `1`

   Theseus leads Ariadne and the other tributes to safety. ☐

   Theseus sees the Minotaur for the first time. ☐

   A dangerous fight begins. ☐

   Ariadne offers help to Theseus. ☐

   Theseus and the other tributes travel to Crete. ☐ `1 mark`

 2f # *Structure Question*

Some STRUCTURE questions ask you to show what different parts of a story are doing, such as setting the scene or describing a character. Try this one out to test your skills.

1. Draw lines to match each part of the story to the correct quotation from the text.

action	**sandy beaches and distant mountains**
past events	**The Minotaur had been imprisoned for years**
setting	**Crete's cruel king, Minos**
character	**Theseus dived sideways**

   `1 mark`

 *Tellastauriuses think that summary and structure questions are great fun. How did you do? Tick a box.*

Flight

Lots of people dream of having wings and being able to fly. When Amina wakes up in the middle of the night to find a pair of wings on her back, the idea is suddenly a reality — so she heads straight outside to test them out...

What to do —

1) Read the story *Flight* — you'll need to turn over for some of it.

2) Now have a big stretch. Reach your arms out to the side, then up high to the ceiling. Just don't get your fingers tangled in the cobwebs up there.

3) All warmed up? Good — you're ready to race on to the questions.

Flight

Amina had always loved to watch birds fly. She admired how they soared high above the rooftops. She was amazed by the shapes they made as they flew in formation towards their destination. Most of all, she loved their sleek, streamlined wings, graceful yet powerful, propelling them onwards through the sky.

The night it happened, Amina hadn't expected anything out of the ordinary. It was the school holidays, and she had spent the day with two of her friends, riding bikes around the local park and watching television. That evening, she had swiftly dropped off to sleep, imagining that the following day would be much the same.

In the dead of night, however, when little could be heard but the scrabbling of a mouse, Amina awoke with a start due to an odd tugging sensation in her back. Twisting around, her fingers touched something curiously soft and downy. She clambered out of bed to look in the mirror and gasped. There on her back, glistening in the moonlight that drifted through her window, was a set of slender wings. They jutted out from behind her shoulder blades, then curved up behind her, almost taller than the top of her head, before reaching down towards her waist. The wings were formed of soft feathers in varying shades of brown, each overlapping the next. When Amina shook her shoulders, the movement rippled down through the feathers until the very last shivered in sympathy with the first.

"Wow," she whispered, in awe of her new, feathered profile.

Suddenly, she heard steps on the landing outside her room. Fearing her mum might come in and see her wings, she rushed towards the safety of her bed. As she did so, her wings clashed with the lamp on her bedside table, causing it to clatter noisily to the floor.

The story continues over the page.

The footsteps stopped.

"Amina?" her mother called from the landing. "Are you okay?"

"Yes, Mum," Amina replied, trying to keep the pain from her voice as she winced from the collision. "I'm fine. I just... tripped. I got up to get a glass of water."

"Be careful," her mother warned automatically, but she sounded reassured. Amina breathed a long sigh of relief as her mother's footsteps slowly padded away.

Rubbing her bruised wing, she pondered her situation. As impossible as it seemed, she really did have wings, and it wasn't an opportunity she wanted to let slip. The valley beyond her house caught her eye through the window, and suddenly she knew exactly what she wanted to do. Tiptoeing lightly, she crept downstairs and out through the back door, making sure to close it behind her to avoid arousing suspicion. Then she ran, pounding across her back garden and into the fields beyond, her bare feet crunching on twigs and dead leaves, before scrambling to the top of a tall hill. She gazed out at the tranquil landscape before her. The whole valley had a blue-black hue, as if a careless hand had swiped a pot of water across a painting, causing all the colours to run.

Mouth set in determination, Amina stretched out her wings and began to run down the hill, her footfalls thudding faster and faster as her wings beat furiously, until, at last, she felt her feet cycle through empty air. She stared down, astonished, at the distinct gap between her feet and the hillside. Her wings kept moving, pushing air away with each powerful downstroke, sending her higher and higher as if she were a puppet on a string. Her whole body felt weightless — it reminded her of swimming underwater, only with cool air rushing past her face instead of salty water.

"I'm flying!" she shouted, breathless with excitement as she sailed through the night sky.

Angling her body, she swept down towards the farmland that carpeted the valley floor. The sheep that littered the fields paused in their bleating to gaze at the unusual winged creature that glided over their heads, larger than any they had seen before. Next, she soared towards the rushing river that carved its path through the valley. From the air, she could see salmon leaping through the current and slippery otters gliding through the dark waters. She whooped with delight and shot off into the distance, dipping down to let her toes trail through the river's cold water as she went.

After a while, she began to feel bolder, and so she headed upwards, ascending further and further until she reached the base of the clouds. The valley shrank to a kaleidoscope of minuscule shapes as she looped her way through the drifts of mist. Suddenly, she felt a presence close by. She looked over and saw a large hawk with sharp talons gliding haughtily through the air. Without warning, reluctant to share its space in the sky with a newcomer, the bird lurched in her direction.

"Hey!" Amina yelled, swerving sharply to avoid a collision. The movement knocked her off balance in the air and she began to plummet through the night sky, frantically trying to right herself before she met the ground. Luckily, she managed to spread her wings and catch herself just in time. After that, she resolved to fly closer to the friendly farm animals occupying the grassy lands below, far from the possibility of an unpleasant encounter.

It was only when she began to feel the warmth of the sun on her face that Amina realised how long she had been outside. She raced urgently back over the fields in the direction of her garden. To ensure she landed gently, she chose a soft patch of grass and drew her wings in slowly as she touched down.

She crept in through the back door and had almost made it to the stairs when she heard the clash of pottery hitting the wooden floor behind her. Turning around, she saw her mum, surrounded by the shards of a broken mug, staring wide-eyed at her daughter, who looked just as she always did — except for a pair of large, feathery wings.

 Open the flap for the start of the story.

2b # Fact Retrieval Questions

For FACT RETRIEVAL questions, you've got to find facts from the text. If you don't spot what you need right away, keep looking 'til you do. Try these ones.

1. Look at the paragraph beginning **'The night it happened...'**

   Give **one** thing Amina did with her friends on the day she got her wings.

   ....

   1 mark

2. What caused Amina to wake up?

She had a bad dream.	She heard a mouse.	She felt a tugging in her back.	She was too hot.

   1 mark

   Circle your answer.

3. Which picture best represents the shape of Amina's wings? Tick **one** box.

   a)   b)   c)   d)

   ☐   ☐   ☐   ☐

   1 mark

4. Read the paragraph beginning **'Suddenly, she heard steps...'**

   Who did Amina think was outside her bedroom?

   ....

   1 mark

5. What happened when Amina rushed back to her bed?

   ....

   1 mark

Unfold these pages before you start

2b
Fact Retrieval Questions

6. What reason did Amina give her mum to explain why she was awake?

1 mark

....

7. Where did Amina go to take off into the air?

| her back garden | the top of a tree | the roof of her house | the top of a hill |

1 mark

Circle your answer.

8. Look at page 35. Where did Amina fly to first?

| the base of the clouds | the river | the farmland | another house |

1 mark

Circle your answer.

9. Look again at page 35.

Complete the table with the animals that Amina saw and where she saw them.

Animals	Where Amina saw them
	in the fields
otters	
hawk	

3 marks

10. What did Amina do to make her landing as gentle as possible? Give **two** things.

....

2 marks

....

Tellastauriuses search high and low to find the facts they need. How about you? Tick to show how you did.

2d

Inference Questions

INFERENCE questions are about things the text doesn't say directly, e.g. what a character feels or what's really happening in a bit of the text. Read 'Flight' again, then try these questions.

1. How does the first paragraph make birds sound impressive? Give **one** way.

    ....

    | 1 mark |

2. Look at page 34.

    How do you know Amina didn't want her mum to know she'd hurt herself?

    ....

    | 1 mark |

3. Look at page 35.

    a) Who or what was the **'unusual winged creature'**?

    ....

    | 1 mark |

    b) How can you tell that the sheep were amazed to see the **'unusual winged creature'**?

    ....

    | 1 mark |

4. Look at page 35. How does the text suggest that the hawk is selfish?

    ....

    | 1 mark |

5. Look at the paragraph beginning **'"Hey!" Amina yelled...'**

    How can you tell Amina was scared by her encounter with the hawk?

    ....

    ....

    | 1 mark |

Inference Questions

6. At what time of day did Amina go back home?

| midnight | midday | sunset | sunrise | 1 mark |

Circle your answer.

7. Look at the last paragraph.

How can you tell that Amina didn't want her parents to know she had been outside the house?

....

1 mark

8. How do you think Amina's mum felt when she saw Amina with wings?

Explain your answer with evidence from the text.

....

....

2 marks

9. How can you tell that Amina liked getting wings and being able to fly?

Use evidence from the text to support your answer.

....

....

....

....

3 marks

Answering inference questions is second nature to a Tellastaurius. How did these pages go for you?

Section 4 — Flight

Word Meaning Questions

2a

For WORD MEANING questions, you've got to think about what words from the text mean. If you're not sure, try reading the whole sentence — it might give you a clue. Have a go at these.

1. **'...when little could be heard but the scrabbling of a mouse...'**

   In this sentence, the word **'scrabbling'** means the same as

   Tick **one** box.

   nibbling ☐

   squeaking ☐

   scratching ☐

   breathing ☐

   1 mark

2. **'She gazed out at the tranquil landscape before her.'**

   What does the word **'tranquil'** mean in this sentence?

   | lively | calm | empty | strange |

   Circle your answer.

   1 mark

3. **'The valley shrank to a kaleidoscope of minuscule shapes...'**

   What does the word **'minuscule'** mean in this sentence?

   ....

   1 mark

4. **'...she began to plummet through the night sky...'**

   What does the word **'plummet'** suggest about how Amina was falling?

   ....

   1 mark

Tellastauriuses can answer word meaning questions while rolling down a hill. How about you? Tick a box.